Let's Talk Maths

for ages 9–11

Andrew Brodie ✓

Contents

This series of three books, will help every school in the delivery of 'a renewed focus on oral and mental mathematics' as recommended in the Rose Review and the Williams Review of Mathematics Teaching.

The Rose Review of the primary curriculum (April 2009) recommends:

> *Primary schools should make sure that children's spoken communication is developed intensively within all subjects and for learning across the curriculum.*

The Review of Mathematics Teaching states that the existing curriculum for mathematics is well balanced and should continue in its current form but it adds:

> *Two issues only are singled out: the need for an increased focus on the 'use and application' of mathematics and on the vitally important question of the classroom discussion of mathematics. It is often suggested that 'mathematics itself is a language' but it must not be overlooked that only by constructive dialogue in the medium of the English language in the classroom can logic and reasoning be fully developed – the factors at the very heart of embedded learning in mathematics.*

In considering pedagogy the Review notes:

> *It must be truly interactive, giving children time, for example, to think, to question as well as answer, to discuss and to try out their own ideas and strategies.*

> *The critical importance of engaging children in discussing mathematics is widely recognised. This, of course, includes learning and using mathematical language. Talking mathematics should not be seen simply as a rehearsal in class of the vocabulary of mathematics, novel and important though that may be for the young learner. It should extend to high quality discussion that develops children's logic, reasoning and deduction skills, and underpins all mathematical learning activity. The ultimate goal is to develop mathematical understanding – comprehension of mathematical ideas and applications.*

How to use this book

Let's Talk Maths provides opportunities for teachers to use, and reuse, stimulating whiteboard displays that encourage pupils to discuss mathematics using appropriate mathematical vocabulary.

Each double-page spread in the teachers' notes features detailed instructions, including questions to prompt discussion, on how to use the CD content and a screenshot of the typical view that the children will see on the interactive whiteboard. The teachers' notes specify the prior learning that the children need, together with learning objectives and success criteria. The notes also give an indication for which Blocks the activity is suitable.

How to use the CD

Choose an activity from the main menu:

Activity navigation:

Main menu

Click on the objective tab to display a child-friendly objective connected to the activity.

Click on the vocabulary tab to display related mathematical vocabulary which should be used as much as possible during the activity.

Click on the instruction tab to display simple, straightforward instructions of what to do. (The teachers' notes provide a detailed description of the activity and suggest questions to prompt discussion.)

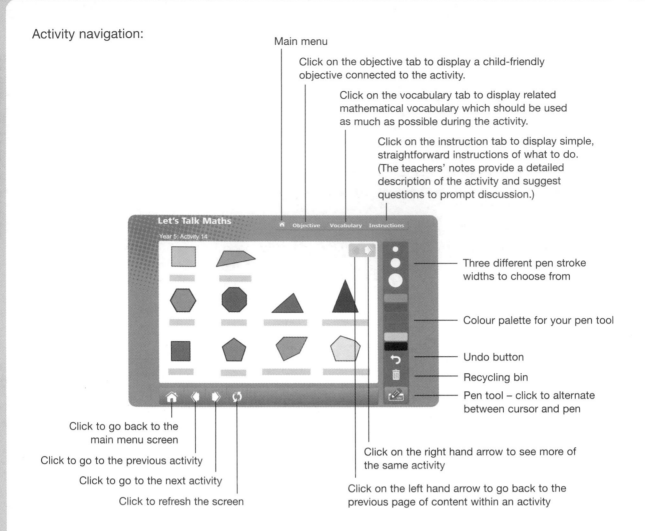

Three different pen stroke widths to choose from

Colour palette for your pen tool

Undo button

Recycling bin

Pen tool – click to alternate between cursor and pen

Click to go back to the main menu screen

Click to go to the previous activity

Click to go to the next activity

Click to refresh the screen

Click on the right hand arrow to see more of the same activity

Click on the left hand arrow to go back to the previous page of content within an activity

Speaking and Listening in Key Stage 2

This is the third book in the series and is designed to be used with children in Years 5 and 6. As you will have read on page 3, the importance of encouraging children to listen carefully and to speak appropriately in all aspects of the curriculum is reflected in national guidance for the teaching of mathematics. Opportunities are found for engaging pupils in speaking and listening activities in each unit of the teaching blocks specified in the Guidance for Planning for Year 5 and Year 6. Suggestions for incorporating most of the learning objectives for 'Speaking', 'Listening and responding' and 'Group discussion and interaction' specified in the Primary Framework for Literacy are linked to specific units for mathematics:

Year 5 Speaking

- Present a spoken argument, sequencing points logically, defending views with evidence and making use of persuasive language
  Block B Unit 2, Block E Units 1 and 3

- Use and explore different question types and different ways words are used, including in formal and informal contexts (Note that this objective is not listed in the guidance for planning but can clearly be addressed on many occasions in discussions of mathematics.)

Year 5 Listening and responding

- Identify different question types and evaluate impact on audience
Block B Units 1 and 3

- Analyse the use of persuasive language
Block A Unit 2

Year 5 Group discussion and interaction

- Plan and manage a group task over time by using different levels of planning
Block C Unit 1, Block D Unit 1

- Understand different ways to take the lead and support others in a group
Block C Unit 3, Block D Unit 3

- Understand the process of decision making
Block A Unit 3, Block C Unit 2, Block D Unit 2, Block E Unit 2

Year 6 Speaking

- Use a range of oral techniques to present persuasive arguments
Block A Unit 1, Block B Units 1 and 3, Block C Unit 2, Block D Unit 1, Block E Unit 3

- Participate in whole-class debate using the conventions and language of debate, including Standard English
Block A Unit 2, Block C Unit 3, Block D Unit 2, Block E Unit 1

Year 6 Listening and responding

- Make notes when listening for a sustained period and discuss how note-taking varies depending on context and purpose
Block C Unit 1

- Analyse and evaluate how speakers present points effectively through use of language, gesture, models and images
Block A Unit 3, Block D Unit 3

Year 6 Group discussion and interaction

- Understand and use a variety of ways to criticise constructively and respond to criticism
Block B Unit 2, Block E Unit 2

- Use time, resources and group members efficiently by distributing tasks, checking progress and making back-up plans
Block B Unit 3, Block C Units 1, 2 and 3, Block E Unit 3

Count from any given whole number in whole-number steps, extending beyond zero when counting backwards; relate the numbers to their position on a number line

Building on previous learning

Before starting this unit check that the children can already:

- [ ] recognise and continue number sequences formed by counting on or back in steps of constant size

- [ ] count on from or back to zero in single-digit steps or multiples of 10

- [ ] use decimal notation for tenths and hundredths and partition decimals

- [ ] position one-place and two-place decimals on a number line

Learning objectives

- Count on from any given whole number in whole-number steps

- Count back from any given whole number in whole-number steps, extending beyond zero

Learning outcomes

The children will be able to:

- read any whole number up to at least 1000

- relate all these to the number line

- use appropriate vocabulary

- talk confidently about the numbers

- count on from any given whole number in whole-number steps

- count back from any given whole number in whole-number steps, extending beyond zero

Success criteria

Can the children...

- [ ] read confidently the numbers pointed out to them?

- [ ] count on from any given whole number in whole-number steps?

- [ ] count back from any given whole number in whole-number steps, extending beyond zero?

- [ ] listen and talk confidently using some of the vocabulary listed and some of the question types shown?

How to use the material for discussion

The adult should start with asking questions to provide a structure but should try to withdraw from the discussion and allow the children to take over so that they are asking questions of each other. They will, at times, need to be reminded of the appropriate vocabulary and you may wish to encourage them to use the vocabulary listed. It would be very helpful to have a class number line that extends all the way round the top of the wall, starting from negative 10 and reaching at least to 1000.

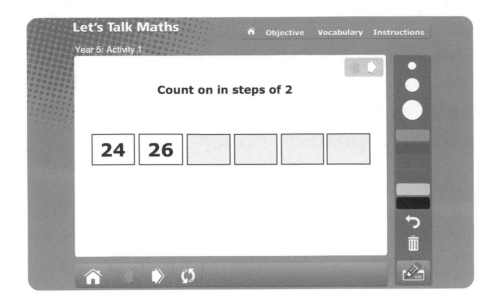

The activity could open with questions of the following type:

- What is this start number? Can you read this start number?
- How many digits does this start number have? Where would we find this number on the class number line?

Now we are going to count on from the start number in steps of … (whatever number is displayed).

You could ask one child to count on in the specified steps, while the others check her/his answers, then ask the child to click on the top right hand arrow for a new start number and a new step number. This child now takes over as leader and invites another child to count on. Some children will see that they could use multiplication to help them.

Once the children are confident with this activity you could increase the challenge by asking them to count back from the start number. The children may need help when the sequence of numbers extends below zero.

Appropriate vocabulary

answer	method	explain
reasoning	reason	predict
relationship	digit	pattern
sequence	place value	ones
tens	hundreds	thousand
one-digit number	two-digit number	three-digit number
four-digit number	positive	negative
above zero	below zero	add
subtract	multiply	plus
minus		

Count from any given number with up to two decimal places in whole-number steps, extending beyond zero when counting backwards; relate the numbers to their position on a number line

Building on previous learning

Before starting this unit check that the children can already:

☐ recognise and continue number sequences formed by counting on or back in steps of constant size

☐ count on from or back to zero in single-digit steps or multiples of 10

☐ count on or back from any given whole number in whole-number steps

☐ use decimal notation for tenths and hundredths and partition decimals

☐ position one-place and two-place decimals on a number line

Learning objectives

- Count on from any given number with up to two decimal places in whole-number steps

- Count back from any given number with up to two decimal places in whole-number steps, extending beyond zero

- Explain what each digit represents in whole numbers and decimals with up to two places

Learning outcomes

The children will be able to:

- read any whole number and numbers with up to two decimal places, up to at least 1000

- relate all these to the number line

- use appropriate vocabulary

- talk confidently about the numbers

- count on from any given number in whole-number steps

- count back from any given number in whole–number steps, extending beyond zero

Success criteria

Can the children...

☐ read confidently the numbers pointed out to them?

☐ count on from any given number in whole-number steps?

☐ count back from any given number in whole-number steps, extending beyond zero?

☐ listen and talk confidently using some of the vocabulary listed and some of the question types shown?

How to use the material for discussion

The adult should start with asking questions to provide a structure but should try to withdraw from the discussion and allow the children to take over so that they are asking questions of each other. This activity follows on from Activity 1 and will help pupils with understanding place value in relation to decimals. Some children will need help with calculations involving adding a whole number, eg 8, to a number such as 87.65 – some are likely to add the 8 units to the 5 hundredths rather than to the 7 units.

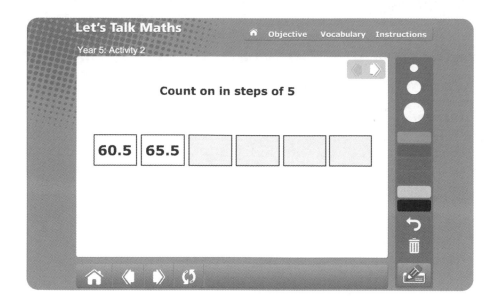

The activity could open with questions of the following type:

- What is this start number? Can you read this start number?
- How many digits does this start number have? Where would we find this number on the class number line? What does each digit in this number represent?

Now we are going to count on from the start number in steps of … (whatever number is on the board).

You could ask one child to count on in the specified steps, while the others check her/his answers, then ask the child to click for a new start number and a new step number. This child now takes over as leader and invites another child to count on. Some children will see that they could use multiplication to help them.

Once the children are confident with this activity you could increase the challenge by asking them to count back from the start number. The children may need some help when the sequence of numbers extends below zero.

Appropriate vocabulary

answer	method	explain
reasoning	reason	predict
relationship	digit	pattern
sequence	decimal point	decimal place
place value	ones	tens
hundreds	thousand	one-digit number
two-digit number	three-digit number	four-digit number
positive	negative	above zero
below zero	add	subtract
multiply	plus	minus

Use knowledge of place value and addition and subtraction of two-digit numbers to derive sums of decimals

Building on previous learning

Before starting this unit check that the children can already:

☐ add or subtract mentally pairs of two-digit whole numbers

☐ use decimal notation for tenths and hundredths and partition decimals

☐ position one-place and two-place decimals on a number line

Learning objectives

■ Use knowledge of place value and addition and subtraction of two-digit numbers to derive sums of decimals

Learning outcomes

The children will be able to:

■ derive the sums of pairs of decimal numbers

■ use appropriate vocabulary

■ talk confidently about the numbers

Success criteria

Can the children…

☐ derive the sums of pairs of decimal numbers?

☐ listen and talk confidently using some of the vocabulary listed and some of the question types shown?

How to use the material for discussion

Children will add together pairs of decimal numbers. As with all of the activities the teacher can start the discussion using appropriate vocabulary and questions but should then encourage the pupils to take turns in leading the discussion. This activity can be repeated regularly and would be very useful as a lesson starter.

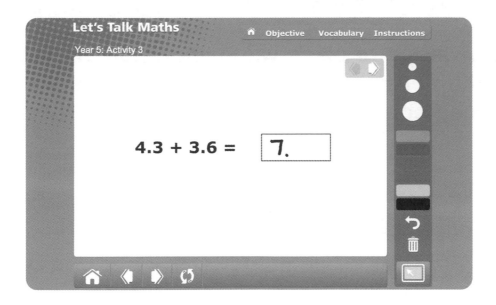

The activity consists of the teacher, or a pupil playing the role of leader, asking pupils to answer questions. Pupils give the answer orally and need to check each other's answers – this is a valuable part of the discussion.

Before asking the pupils to find the answers to the addtitions, encourage them to look closely at each of the numbers. What is the value of the ones (or units) digit? What is the value of the tenths digit?

Now encourage the children to explain how they could add the numbers together. Are they going to add the ones first? Are they going to add the tenths first? Are they going to add the ones from the second number to the first number, then add the tenths? Are they going to add the tenths from the second number to the first number, then add the ones? Which way do they find quickest?

Appropriate vocabulary

calculate	calculation	equation
operation	answer	method
explain	reasoning	pattern
predict	reason	rule
place value	partition	digit
two-digit number	three-digit number	add
sum	total	plus
sequence	decimal point	decimal place
ones	tenths	

Use knowledge of place value and addition and subtraction of two-digit numbers to derive differences between decimals

Building on previous learning

Before starting this unit check that the children can already:

☐ add or subtract mentally pairs of two-digit whole numbers

☐ use decimal notation for tenths and hundredths and partition decimals

☐ position one-place and two-place decimals on a number line

Learning objectives

■ Use knowledge of place value and addition and subtraction of two-digit numbers to derive differences between decimals

Learning outcomes

The children will be able to:

■ find differences between pairs of decimal numbers

■ use appropriate vocabulary

■ talk confidently about the numbers

Success criteria

Can the children…

☐ derive the differences between pairs of decimal numbers?

☐ listen and talk confidently using some of the vocabulary listed and some of the question types shown?

How to use the material for discussion

Children will find the difference between two decimal numbers. As with all of the activities the teacher can start the discussion using appropriate vocabulary and questions but should then encourage the pupils to take turns in leading the discussion. This activity can be repeated regularly and would be very useful as a lesson starter.

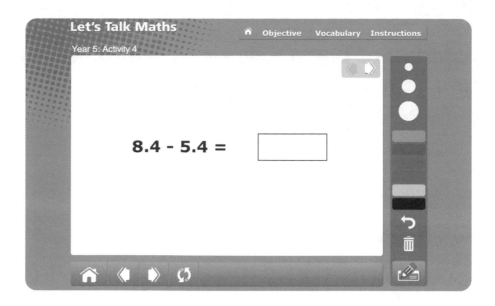

The activity consists of the teacher, or a pupil playing the role of leader, asking pupils to find the difference between two decimal numbers. Pupils give the answer orally and need to check each other's answers – this is a valuable part of the discussion.

Before asking the pupils to find the differences between the two numbers, encourage them to look closely at each of the numbers. What is the value of the ones (or units) digit? What is the value of the tenths digit?

Now encourage the children to explain how they could find the differences between them. Are they going to count on in tenths and ones from the smaller to the greater number? Are they going to count back? Are they going to use an empty number line? Which way do they find quickest?

Appropriate vocabulary

calculate	calculation	equation
operation	answer	method
explain	reasoning	pattern
predict	reason	rule
place value	partition	digit
two-digit number	three-digit number	subtract
minus	difference	
sequence	decimal point	decimal place
ones	tenths	

Use knowledge of place value and addition and subtraction of two-digit numbers to derive doubles of decimals

Building on previous learning

Before starting this unit check that the children can already:

- [ ] add or subtract mentally pairs of two-digit whole numbers
- [ ] use decimal notation for tenths and hundredths and partition decimals
- [ ] position one-place and two-place decimals on a number line
- [ ] use knowledge of place value and addition and subtraction of two-digit numbers to derive sums and differences of decimals

Learning objectives

- Use knowledge of place value and addition and subtraction of two-digit numbers to derive doubles of decimals

Learning outcomes

The children will be able to:

- find doubles of decimal numbers
- use appropriate vocabulary
- talk confidently about the numbers

Success criteria

Can the children…

- [ ] derive the doubles of decimal numbers?
- [ ] listen and talk confidently using some of the vocabulary listed and some of the question types shown?

How to use the material for discussion

In this activity children will double decimal numbers. As with all of the activities the teacher can start the discussion using appropriate vocabulary and questions but should then encourage the pupils to take turns in leading the discussion. This activity can be repeated regularly and would be very useful as a lesson starter.

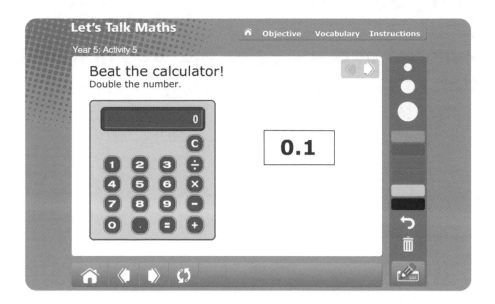

The activity consists of the teacher, or a pupil playing the role of leader, asking pupils to double decimal numbers. Pupils give the answer orally and need to check each other's answers – this is a valuable part of the discussion. One of the pupils should use the calculator so that you can establish a competition between the calculator and the brain! You will need to check that the children know which buttons to press to find doubles – it is a valuable learning experience for pupils to realise that they can multiply by 2 or add the number to itself to achieve the same result.

Encourage the children to explain how they double the number. Do they add on? Which digit do they double first? Which way do they find quickest?

Appropriate vocabulary

calculate	calculation	equation
operation	answer	method
explain	reasoning	pattern
predict	reason	rule
place value	partition	digit
two-digit number	three-digit number	double
sequence	decimal point	decimal place
ones	tenths	

Use knowledge of place value and addition and subtraction of two-digit numbers to derive halves of decimals (1)

Building on previous learning

Before starting this unit check that the children can already:

- [ ] add or subtract mentally pairs of two-digit whole numbers
- [ ] use decimal notation for tenths and hundredths and partition decimals
- [ ] position one-place and two-place decimals on a number line
- [ ] use knowledge of place value and addition and subtraction of two-digit numbers to derive sums, differences and doubles of decimals

Learning objectives

- Use knowledge of place value and addition and subtraction of two-digit numbers to derive halves of decimals

Learning outcomes

The children will be able to:

- find halves of decimal numbers
- use appropriate vocabulary
- talk confidently about the numbers

Success criteria

Can the children…

- [ ] derive the halves of decimal numbers?
- [ ] listen and talk confidently using some of the vocabulary listed and some of the question types shown?

How to use the material for discussion

In this activity children will halve decimal numbers. This activity features decimal numbers that are relatively easy to halve as each tenth digit is an even numeral. Note that we have included numbers such as 6.0 – pupils need to understand that this has the same value as 6 but is presented in a different format.

As with all of the activities the teacher can start the discussion using appropriate vocabulary and questions but should then encourage the pupils to take turns in leading the discussion. This activity can be repeated regularly and would be very useful as a lesson starter.

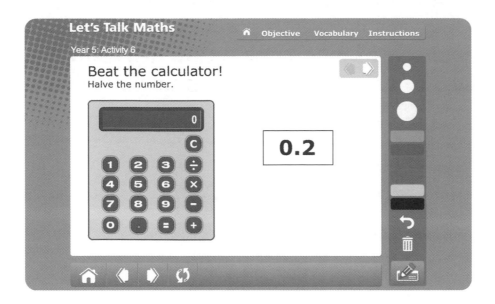

The activity consists of the teacher, or a pupil playing the role of leader, asking pupils to halve decimal numbers. Pupils give the answer orally and need to check each other's answers – this is a valuable part of the discussion. One of the pupils should use the calculator so that you can establish a competition between the calculator and the brain! You will need to check that the children know which buttons to press to find halves – it is a valuable learning experience for pupils to realise that they can divide by 2 or multiply by 0.5 to achieve the same result.

Encourage the children to explain how they halve the number. Which digit do they halve first? What happens when the units digit is an odd number? Which way do they find quickest?

Appropriate vocabulary

calculate	calculation	equation
operation	answer	method
explain	reasoning	pattern
predict	reason	rule
place value	partition	digit
two-digit number	three-digit number	double
sequence	decimal point	decimal place
ones	tenths	

Use knowledge of place value and addition and subtraction of two-digit numbers to derive halves of decimals (2)

Building on previous learning

Before starting this unit check that the children can already:

☐ add or subtract mentally pairs of two-digit whole numbers

☐ use decimal notation for tenths and hundredths and partition decimals

☐ position one-place and two-place decimals on a number line

☐ use knowledge of place value and addition and subtraction of two-digit numbers to derive sums, differences and doubles of decimals

Learning objectives

- Use knowledge of place value and addition and subtraction of two-digit numbers to derive halves of decimals

Learning outcomes

The children will be able to:

- find halves of decimal numbers
- use appropriate vocabulary
- talk confidently about the numbers

Success criteria

Can the children…

☐ derive the halves of decimal numbers?

☐ listen and talk confidently using some of the vocabulary listed and some of the question types shown?

How to use the material for discussion

In this activity, children will halve decimal numbers. This activity follows on from Activity 6 but features more difficult examples as well as some of the examples that pupils have met previously.

As with all of the activities the teacher can start the discussion using appropriate vocabulary and questions but should then encourage the pupils to take turns in leading the discussion. This activity can be repeated regularly and would be very useful as a lesson starter.

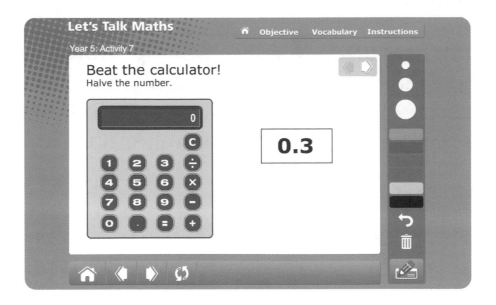

The activity consists of the teacher, or a pupil playing the role of leader, asking pupils to halve decimal numbers. Pupils give the answer orally and need to check each other's answers – this is a valuable part of the discussion. One of the pupils should use the calculator so that you can establish a competition between the calculator and the brain! You will need to check that the children know which buttons to press to find halves – it is a valuable learning experience for pupils to realise that they can divide by 2 or multiply by 0.5 to achieve the same result.

Encourage the children to explain how they halve the number. Which digit do they halve first? What happens when the tenths digit is an odd number? What happens when the units digit is an odd number? What happens when both digits are odd numbers? Which way do they find quickest?

Appropriate vocabulary

calculate	calculation	equation
operation	answer	method
explain	reasoning	pattern
predict	reason	rule
place value	partition	digit
two-digit number	three-digit number	double
sequence	decimal point	decimal place
ones	tenths	

Count from any given number with up to two decimal places in whole number and decimal steps, extending beyond zero when counting backwards; relate the numbers to their position on a number line

Building on previous learning

Before starting this unit check that the children can already:

- [ ] recognise and continue number sequences formed by counting on or back in steps of constant size
- [ ] count on or back from any given whole number or decimal with up to two places in whole-number steps
- [ ] use decimal notation for tenths and hundredths and partition decimals
- [ ] position one-place and two-place decimals on a number line
- [ ] use knowledge of place value and addition and subtraction of two-digit numbers to derive sums and differences and doubles and halves of decimals

Learning objectives

- Count on from any given number with up to two decimal places in whole-number and decimal steps
- Count back from any given number with up to two decimal places in whole-number and decimal steps, extending beyond zero
- Explain what each digit represents in whole numbers and decimals with up to two places

Learning outcomes

The children will be able to:

- read any whole number and numbers with up to two decimal places, up to at least 1000
- relate all these to the number line
- use appropriate vocabulary
- talk confidently about the numbers
- count on from any given number in whole-number and decimal steps
- count back from any given number in whole-number and decimal steps, extending beyond zero

Success criteria

Can the children…

- [ ] read confidently the numbers pointed out to them?
- [ ] count on from any given number in whole-number and decimal steps?
- [ ] count back from any given number in whole-number and decimal steps, extending beyond zero?
- [ ] listen and talk confidently using some of the vocabulary listed and some of the question types shown?

How to use the material for discussion

This activity follows on from Activities 1 and 2 and will help pupils with understanding place value in relation to decimals. Pupils will find this activity easier with the experience that they have gained from Activities 3 to 7. However, it becomes particularly difficult where decimal numbers are being added to numbers with two places of decimals.

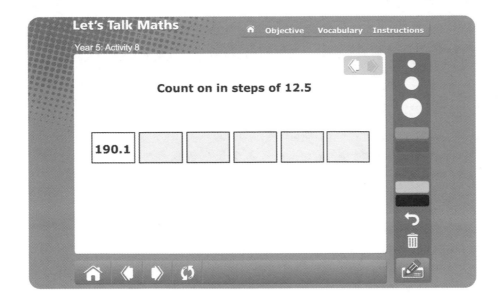

The activity could open with questions of the following type:

- What is this start number? Can you read this start number?
- How many digits does this start number have?
- Where would we find this number on the class number line?
- What does each digit in this number represent?

Now we are going to count on from the start number in steps of … (whatever number is displayed on the whiteboard).

You could ask one child to count on in the specified steps, while the others check her/his answers, then ask the child to click for a new start number and a new step number. This child now takes over as leader and invites another child to count on.

Once the children are confident with this first activity you could increase the challenge by asking them to say what number they would reach by counting on from the start number by three steps, four steps, five steps, ten steps. Some children will see that they could use multiplication to help them.

Now start the activity again, perhaps on another day, this time counting back to the start number.

Appropriate vocabulary

answer	method	explain
reasoning	reason	predict
relationship	digit	pattern
sequence	decimal point	decimal place
place value	ones	tens
hundreds	thousand	one-digit number
two-digit number	three-digit number	four-digit number
positive	negative	above zero
below zero	add	subtract
multiply	plus	minus

Recall quickly multiplication facts up to 10 x 10

Building on previous learning

Before starting this unit check that the children can already:

☐ derive and recall multiplication facts for the 2, 3, 4, 5, 6, 7, 8, 9 and 10 times tables and related division facts

Learning objectives

- recall quickly multiplication facts up to 10 x 10
- use the multiplication facts to derive quickly corresponding division facts

Learning outcomes

The children will be able to:

- recall quickly all multiplication and division facts up to 10 x 10

Success criteria

Can the children…

☐ respond quickly to the multiplication question shown on screen?

☐ find related division facts?

How to use the material for discussion

By the time they have reached Year 5, pupils will have constructed the multiplication tables up to 10 x 10 and will have found the corresponding division facts. This activity concerns raising pupils' confidence in mental arithmetic skills by encouraging rapid recall of multiplication facts. Practising number facts, understanding the vocabulary and methods of recording, can give pupils the tools with which to deal with more complex mathematical problems.

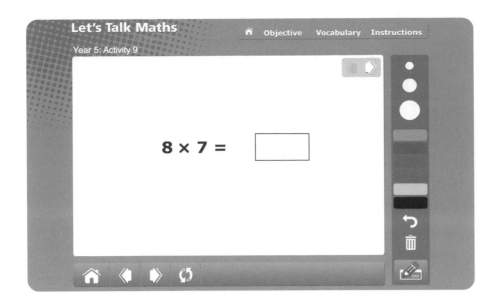

Ask the pupils to take turns to come to the whiteboard to generate multiplication questions. You may wish to set a time challenge for them to answer each question. Can they beat the calculator? (Where one pupil uses the calculator and another works mentally.) Alternatively you could ask them to see how many questions that they can answer in one minute.

On another occasion ask the pupils to find the answer to one question then to create a division fact related to that question. For example the question 5 x 8 has the answer 40, which the pupils can then use to create two possible division questions: 40 ÷ 8 and 40 ÷ 5.

This activity also provides a useful opportunity to extend pupils' vocabulary:

- 40 is the product of 5 and 8
- 40 is a multiple of 5
- 40 is a multiple of 8
- 5 is the quotient when 40 is divided by 8 (8 is the divisor)
- 8 is the quotient when 40 is divided by 5 (5 is the divisor)

Pupils could point out where the product is a square number.

Appropriate vocabulary		
pair	multiply	divide
equals	times	product
quotient	calculate	calculation
operation	answer	multiple
divisor	square number	

Use the multiplication facts to multiply pairs of multiples of 10 and 100

Building on previous learning

Before starting this unit check that the children can already:

☐ recall quickly multiplication facts up to 10 x 10

☐ use the multiplication facts to derive quickly corresponding division facts

Learning objectives

- recall quickly multiplication facts up to 10 x 10
- use the multiplication facts to multiply pairs of multiples of 10 and 100

Learning outcomes

The children will be able to:

- recall quickly all multiplication and division facts up to 10 x 10
- use the multiplication facts to multiply pairs of multiples of 10 and 100

Success criteria

Can the children…

☐ respond quickly to the multiplication question shown on screen?

☐ find related division facts?

How to use the material for discussion

By the time they have reached Year 5, pupils will have constructed the multiplication tables up to 10 x 10 and will have found the corresponding division facts. This activity concerns raising pupils' confidence in mental arithmetic skills by encouraging rapid recall of multiplication facts and using these facts to multiply pairs of multiples of 10 and 100 – this will also strengthen pupils' understanding of place value.

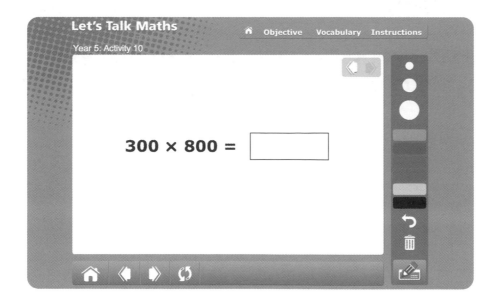

This activity could open with questions of the following type:

- Can you multiply multiples of 10 and 100?
- How quickly can you answer this question?

Ask the pupils to take turns to come to the whiteboard to work out multiplication questions. Most pupils find this activity much more difficult than finding the multiplication facts up to 10 x 10. Discourage them from saying 'you just add a zero' or 'you just add two zeroes', but instead to use understanding of place value to consider that multiplying by 10 or by 100 moves the positions of the numbers.

If the pupils are confident you may wish to set a time challenge for them to answer each question. Can they beat the calculator? (Where one pupil uses the calculator and another works mentally.) Alternatively you could ask them to see how many questions that they can answer in 30 seconds.

On another occasion ask the pupils to find the answer to one question then to create a division fact related to that question. For example the question 20 x 300 has the answer 6000, which the pupils can then use to create two possible division questions: 6000 ÷ 20 and 6000 ÷ 300.

Appropriate vocabulary

pair	multiply	divide
equals	times	product
quotient	calculate	calculation
operation	answer	multiple
divisor	square number	place value

Year 5 Activity 11

Use understanding of place value to multiply whole numbers and decimals by 10, 100 or 1000

Building on previous learning

Before starting this unit check that the children can already:

☐ recall quickly multiplication facts up to 10 x 10

☐ use the multiplication facts to derive quickly corresponding division facts

☐ use the multiplication facts to multiply pairs of multiples of 10 and 100

Learning objectives

■ use understanding of place value to multiply whole numbers and decimals by 10, 100 or 1000

Learning outcomes

The children will be able to:

■ use understanding of place value to multiply whole numbers and decimals by 10, 100 or 1000

Success criteria

Can the children…

☐ find the answer to the multiplication question shown on screen?

☐ use understanding of place value to multiply whole numbers and decimals by 10?

☐ use understanding of place value to multiply whole numbers and decimals by 100?

☐ use understanding of place value to multiply whole numbers and decimals by 1000?

How to use the material for discussion

By the time they have reached Year 5, pupils will have constructed the multiplication tables up to 10 x 10 and will have found the corresponding division facts. This activity extends pupils' mental arithmetic skills by requiring them to consider place value when multiplying by 10, 100 or 1000. They will already have experienced multiplying a whole number by 10 resulting in an answer with a zero in the units (ones) column. They will now discover that multiplying a decimal by 10 does not cause the introduction of a zero.

Let's Talk Maths

Year 5: Activity 11

Objective   Vocabulary   Instructions

Can you multiply by 10, 100 or 1000?

$$0.7 \times 100 = \boxed{}$$

Ask the pupils to take turns to come to the whiteboard to work out multiplication questions. This activity is useful in showing pupils that 'just adding a zero' or 'just adding two zeroes' simply won't work, but instead they need to use their understanding of place value to see that multiplying by 10, 100 or 1000 moves the positions of the numbers.

If the pupils are confident you may wish to set a time challenge for them to answer each question. Can they beat the calculator? (Where one pupil uses the calculator and another works mentally.) Alternatively you could ask them to see how many questions that they can answer in 30 seconds.

You may like to take the opportunity of introducing the word 'integer', ensuring that the pupils understand that numbers such as 0.4, 3.8 and 7.9 are not integers because they are not whole numbers.

Appropriate vocabulary

more	less	total
pair	multiply	divide
equals	times	product
place value	calculate	calculation
operation	answer	multiple
decimal	decimal point	decimal place
integer		

Use understanding of place value to divide whole numbers and decimals by 10 or 100

Building on previous learning

Before starting this unit check that the children can already:

- [ ] recall quickly multiplication facts up to 10 x 10
- [ ] use the multiplication facts to derive quickly corresponding division facts
- [ ] use the multiplication facts to multiply pairs of multiples of 10 and 100
- [ ] use understanding of place value to multiply whole numbers and decimals by 10, 100 or 1000

Learning objectives

- use understanding of place value to divide whole numbers and decimals by 10 or 100

Learning outcomes

The children will be able to:

- use understanding of place value to divide whole numbers and decimals by 10 or 100

Success criteria

Can the children…

- [ ] find the answer to the division question shown on screen?
- [ ] use understanding of place value to divide whole numbers and decimals by 10?
- [ ] use understanding of place value to divide whole numbers and decimals by 100?

How to use the material for discussion

By the time they have reached Year 5, pupils will have constructed the multiplication tables up to 10 x 10 and will have found the corresponding division facts. This activity extends pupils' mental arithmetic skills by requiring them to consider place value when dividing by 10 or 100. Note that we have not included dividing by 1000 as this will result in answers with 4 decimal places but you could extend the activity for more able pupils.

Let's Talk Maths

Year 5: Activity 12

Objective   Vocabulary   Instructions

Can you divide by 10 or 100?

$$460 \div 100 = \boxed{}$$

Ask the pupils to take turns to come to the whiteboard to work out division questions. Pupils will need to concentrate very hard to complete these questions, realising that dividing by 10 results in the digits moving one place to the right and dividing by 100 results in moving two places to the right. Note that some of the answers will be numbers with three decimal places.

If the pupils are confident you may wish to set a time challenge for them to answer each question. Can they beat the calculator? (Where one pupil uses the calculator and another works mentally.) Alternatively you could ask them to see how many questions that they can answer in 30 seconds.

You may like to revise the word 'integer', ensuring that the pupils understand that numbers such as 9.2, 8.4 and 0.5 are not integers because they are not whole numbers.

Appropriate vocabulary

pair	multiply	divide
equals	times	product
place value	calculate	calculation
operation	answer	multiple
decimal	decimal point	decimal place
integer		

Solve one-step and two-step problems involving whole numbers and decimals and all four operations, choosing and using appropriate calculation strategies, including calculator use

Building on previous learning

Before starting this unit check that the children can already:

☐ derive and recall all addition and subtraction facts for each number to at least 20

☐ derive and recall sums and differences of multiples of 10, 100 or 1000

☐ derive and recall all number pairs that total 100

☐ recall quickly multiplication facts up to 10 x 10

☐ use the multiplication facts to derive quickly corresponding division facts

☐ use knowledge of rounding, place value, number facts and inverse operations to estimate and check calculations

Learning objectives

■ Solve problems involving adding in the context of money

■ Solve problems involving subtracting in the context of money

■ Solve problems involving multiplying in the context of money

■ Solve problems involving dividing in the context of money

■ Solve one-step problems such as finding the total of or the difference between two amounts of money

■ Solve two-step problems such as finding the total of two amounts of money then finding the difference between them

Learning outcomes

The children will be able to:

■ find total amounts by adding or multiplying

■ compare two amounts by finding the difference

■ divide amounts of money by 2

Success criteria

Can the children…

☐ use addition and/or multiplication to find total amounts?

☐ use subtraction to make comparisons between two amounts?

☐ use division to share amounts equally?

☐ choose and use appropriate calculation strategies, including calculator use?

☐ use the calculator efficiently and interpret the display correctly in the context of money?

☐ use appropriate vocabulary in relation to spending money and finding change?

How to use the material for discussion

The chart provides many opportunities for discussion and extended activities involving solving problems using all four rules.

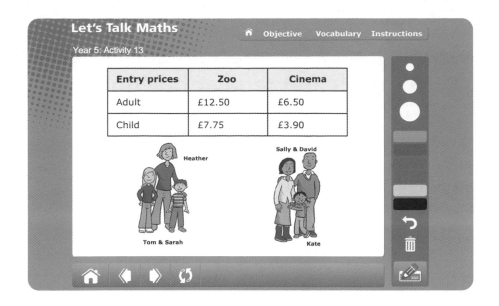

This activity provides many opportunities for creating and solving problems. You could ask the children to create some problems for others to solve. Here are some ideas:

- What is the total cost for Heather and her family to visit the zoo? Would Sally's family pay more or less to visit the zoo? Why?
- What is the total cost for Sally and her family to visit the cinema? How much cheaper than visiting the zoo is this?
- Heather suggests that both families visit the zoo, then share the cost equally – what would each family pay?
- How much would it cost for 5 children to visit the cinema?

Appropriate vocabulary

more	less	total
cost	altogether	difference
price	change	double
answer	explain	operation
pound	penny	pence
coin	add	subtract
multiply	double	calculate
note	calculator	more expensive
less expensive	compare	

Identify, visualise and describe properties of rectangles, triangles and regular polygons

Building on previous learning

Before starting this unit check that the children can already:

- [ ] visualise and name common 2-D shapes and describe their features
- [ ] sort, make and describe shapes referring to their properties
- [ ] identify reflective symmetry in patterns and 2-D shapes
- [ ] draw polygons and classify them by identifying their properties, including their line symmetry

Learning objectives

- Identify, visualise and describe properties of rectangles, triangles and regular polygons

Learning outcomes

The children will be able to:

- identify 2-D shapes on screen
- use appropriate vocabulary to refer to the properties of the shapes
- identify, visualise and describe the following shapes: square, scalene triangle, equilateral triangle, isosceles triangle, rectangle, quadrilateral, regular pentagon, irregular pentagon, regular hexagon, irregular hexagon, regular heptagon, irregular heptagon, regular octagon, irregular octagon, circle, semicircle.

Success criteria

Can the children…

- [ ] identify 2-D shapes, using appropriate vocabulary to refer to their properties?
- [ ] describe the properties of the following shapes: square, scalene triangle, equilateral triangle, isosceles triangle, rectangle, quadrilateral, regular pentagon, irregular pentagon, regular hexagon, irregular hexagon, regular heptagon, irregular heptagon, regular octagon, irregular octagon, circle, semicircle?

How to use the material for discussion

The task is for the pupils to identify each shape and describe its properties. Note that the framework refers to regular polygons but we have included irregular polygons to encourage the pupils to recognise the attributes of regular shapes.

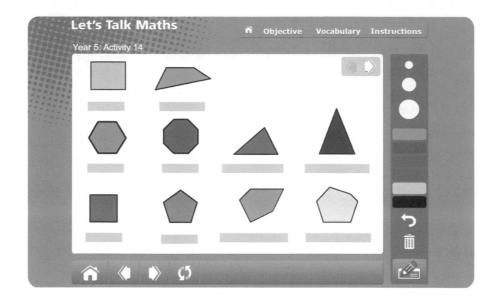

For each shape, ask one of the children to describe one property that the shape possesses (but not name the shape), eg the number of sides or the number of vertices. Ask another pupil to describe a different property of the shape. Encourage the children to state whether the sides are equal in length and whether the shape has reflective symmetry. Once all the properties of the shape have been discussed ask the pupils to give the name of the shape. Then click the grey box under the shape to reveal the name. Note that there are several quadrilaterals, including squares and rectangles in different orientations.

Appropriate vocabulary

triangle	quadrilateral	rectangle
hexagon	corner	side
straight	curved	shape
line of symmetry	mirror line	reflection
square	rectangular	triangular
pentagon	octagon	edge
property	explain	describe
circle	semicircle	symmetrical
reflective symmetry	right-angled	vertex
vertices	regular	irregular
polygon	side	parallel
perpendicular	angle	isosceles
scalene	equilateral	

Read and plot coordinates in the first quadrant

Building on previous learning

Before starting this unit check that the children can already:

☐ visualise and name common 2-D shapes and describe their features

☐ recognise horizontal and vertical lines

☐ describe and identify the position of a square on a grid of squares

Learning objectives

■ Read and plot coordinates in the first quadrant

Learning outcomes

The children will be able to:

■ read and plot coordinates in the first quadrant

■ use appropriate vocabulary in relation to coordinates

Success criteria

Can the children…

☐ use appropriate vocabulary: coordinates, x-axis, y-axis, origin, x-coordinate, y-coordinate?

☐ read and plot coordinates in the first quadrant?

How to use the material for discussion

The grid shows the x-axis and y-axis together with four red dots labelled A, B, C and D. The pupils' task is to identify the coordinates of the four red dots and then, following spoken instruction, to drag on to the grid dots E, F, G, H, I and J.

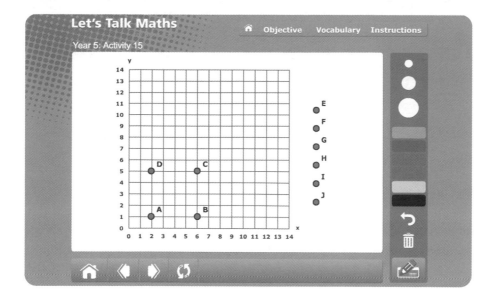

Encourage the children to use the technical vocabulary accurately, ensuring that they use all of the following terms: coordinates, x-axis, y-axis, origin, x-coordinate, y-coordinate

In identifying coordinates the pupils may need clues to remind them to find the x-coordinate before the y-coordinate:

- eg 'crack the eggs (x) before you find the yolk (y)'
- or 'along the corridor then up the stairs'

Note that, in Year 4, the pupils will have described and identified the position of a square on a grid of squares but they are now required to identify the position of a point where a horizontal line crosses a vertical line.

Ask one child to lead the discussion when the points E, F, G, H, I and J can be added to the grid. He/she could ask one of the other pupils to give instructions where to place each 'dot' – in this way the children will need to use the correct vocabulary as well as to give the coordinates in the correct order while the others check that they have done so.

Appropriate vocabulary

coordinates	horizontal	vertical
perpendicular	parallel	x-axis
y-axis	x-coordinate	y-coordinate
origin		

Estimate and measure acute and obtuse angles using a protractor to a suitable degree of accuracy

Building on previous learning

Before starting this unit check that the children can already:

☐ use appropriate units to estimate, measure and record measurements of length to the nearest centimetre

☐ read, to the nearest division and half-division, scales that are numbered or partially numbered

Learning objectives

- Estimate and measure acute and obtuse angles using a protractor to a suitable degree of accuracy
- Interpret a reading that lies between two unnumbered divisions on a scale

Learning outcomes

The children will be able to:

- use a picture of a protractor as an aid to developing their vocabulary in relation to measurement of angles
- measure to the nearest degree using a real protractor
- identify whether an angle is acute or obtuse
- make reasonable estimates of sizes of angles

Success criteria

Can the children…

☐ identify whether an angle is acute or obtuse?

☐ make reasonable estimates of sizes of angles?

☐ use a protractor correctly to measure angles?

☐ use appropriate vocabulary in relation to measurement of angles?

How to use the material for discussion

Reading a protractor is a skill that pupils of all ages can find extremely difficult, often because they have never looked closely at the way the protractor is marked. This activity provides the opportunity to explain and use a protractor. Pupils will measure angles in relation to the protractor.

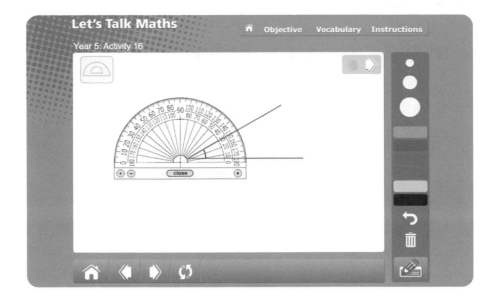

Ask the children whether the angle displayed is acute (between 0° and 90°) or obtuse (between 90° and 180°), then to estimate the size of the angle. Once an estimated size has been agreed, ask a child to drag the protractor over the angle to measure it. Watch carefully how the pupil places the protractor – encourage her/him to position the central cross-hair exactly over the point where the two lines meet to make the angle. The next important step is to position one of the protractor's zero lines over one of the lines of the angle then to read round the protractor from that zero.

Now ask one of the children to become the leader of the discussion.

It is essential that you continue this work with real protractors. Encourage the children to measure random angles that you have prepared for them. They should estimate the angles before measuring them accurately as the estimate will provide a clue that they have used the protractor incorrectly if they produce an unexpected size for the angle.

Appropriate vocabulary

measure	angle	protractor
approximate	estimate	degree
right angle	acute	obtuse

Calculate angles in a straight line

Building on previous learning

Before starting this unit check that the children can already:

☐ estimate and measure acute and obtuse angles using a protractor to a suitable degree of accuracy

Learning objectives

■ Calculate angles in a straight line

Learning outcomes

The children will be able to:

■ identify whether an angle is acute or obtuse

■ make reasonable estimates of sizes of angles

■ calculate the size of a missing angle where one angle of a pair of angles on a straight line is given

Success criteria

Can the children…

☐ identify whether an angle is acute or obtuse?

☐ make reasonable estimates of sizes of angles?

☐ use appropriate vocabulary in relation to measurement of angles?

☐ calculate the size of a missing angle where one angle of a pair of angles on a straight line is given?

How to use the material for discussion

Having experienced measuring angles with a protractor the pupils should now be skilled in estimating the sizes of angles. They will be aware that angles on a straight line have a total measurement of 180°. This activity provides practice in subtracting from 180 to find the size of an angle where one angle of a pair of angles on a straight line is given.

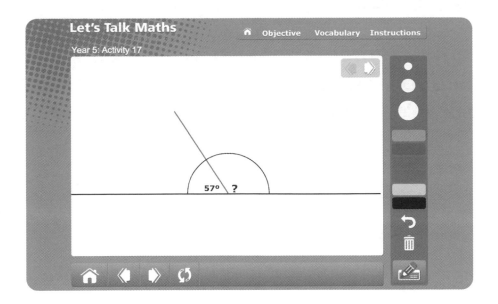

Ask the children to state whether the angle shown is acute (between 0° and 90°) or obtuse (between 90° and 180°), then to state whether the missing angle is acute or obtuse (it will be the opposite to the angle shown). Now ask the children to find the size of the missing angle – they may not realise at first that it can be found by subtracting the size of the given angle from 180°. If necessary you could provide the children with calculators but, if possible, encourage them to calculate using mental methods.

Now ask one of the children to become the leader of the discussion.

Appropriate vocabulary

measure	angle	protractor
approximate	estimate	degree
right angle	acute	obtuse
subtract		

Calculate the perimeter of regular polygons; use the formula for the area of a rectangle to calculate the rectangle's area

Building on previous learning

Before starting this unit check that the children can already:

☐ draw rectangles and find their perimeters

☐ find the area of rectangles by counting squares

Learning objectives

■ Draw rectangles and measure and calculate their perimeters

■ Find the area of rectilinear shapes drawn on a square grid by counting squares

Learning outcomes

The children will be able to:

■ find perimeters by calculating

■ find the area of rectangles by using the appropriate formula

Success criteria

Can the children…

☐ find perimeters of rectangles by measuring and calculating?

☐ find the area of rectangles by using the appropriate formula?

☐ use appropriate vocabulary in relation to perimeter and area?

How to use the material for discussion

Ask pupils how they find the perimeters of the rectangles shown by adding the lengths of the sides. Pupils should also describe how they find the areas by multiplying the length by the width.

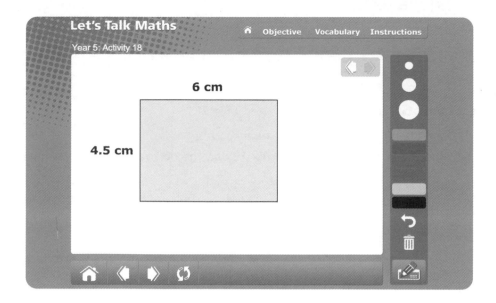

Explain that the rectangle shown on the whiteboard is a picture of a rectangle with two of its sides marked in centimetres – ensure that the pupils understand that it is only a picture and that centimetres are much smaller than those illustrated!

Explain that the distance around a shape is called its perimeter – you may wish to mention that the fence around the school could be described as the perimeter fence. Ask the pupils how they can find the perimeter of the rectangle – hopefully they will state that the lengths of the sides can all be added together.

Now ask one of the children to become the leader of the discussion in relation to a different rectangle.

On a different occasion you can use the same material to discuss area, reminding pupils that area is measured in square centimetres. If the pupils are not already aware of the formula to find the area of a rectangle you could show them a rectangle drawn on squared paper and point out that the area can be found by counting squares or by multiplying the length by the width. Once you feel that the pupils are confident with this, use the activity above but this time ask the pupils to find the area of each rectangle.

Appropriate vocabulary

perimeter	area	centimetre
square centimetre	grid	rectangle
length	distance	ruler
measure	measurement	

Blocks D and revision

Use a calendar to calculate time intervals

Building on previous learning

Before starting this unit check that the children can already:

☐ derive and recall multiplication facts up to 10 x 10 and the corresponding division facts

Learning objectives

■ Use a calendar to calculate time intervals

Learning outcomes

The children will be able to:

■ find the number of days between two events by referring to the calendar

■ convert days to weeks and days by dividing by 7

■ state that a leap year has 366 days and that other years have 365 days and that the month of February has 29 days in a leap year and 28 days in other years

Success criteria

Can the children…

☐ state the number of days in each month?

☐ identify the special features of a leap year?

☐ use the calendar to calculate time intervals?

☐ convert time intervals measured in number of days to time intervals measured in weeks and days?

How to use the material for discussion

The calendar is for the year 2012, a leap year. The pupils' task is to find time intervals between different dates on the calendar. Many children will not know the number of days in each month and this activity presents the opportunity for them to discuss and learn these.

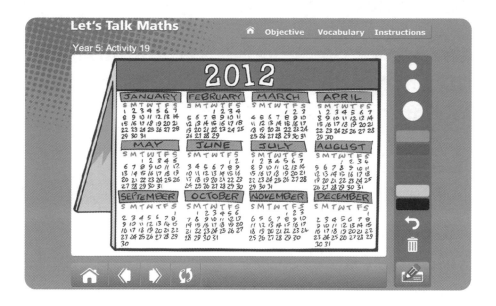

Ask the children to find time intervals between specified dates. For example, two children could state the dates of their birthdays and the time interval between the two dates can be calculated in days. Can the children work out how to change this to weeks and days?

Can the children say what is special about the year 2012? There may be several special aspects of the year but ensure that they notice that it is a leap year – leap years take place every four years, except at the turn of a century unless the new century is a multiple of 4 (eg 1600, 2000).

Appropriate vocabulary

January	February	March
April	May	June
July	August	September
October	November	December
year	month	leap year
calendar	time interval	century
decade		

Use knowledge of place value and multiplication facts to 10 x 10 to derive related multiplication facts involving decimals

Building on previous learning

Before starting this unit check that the children can already:

☐ recall quickly multiplication facts up to 10 x 10

☐ use the multiplication facts to derive quickly corresponding division facts

Learning objectives

■ use the multiplication facts to derive multiplication facts involving decimals

Learning outcomes

The children will be able to:

■ recall quickly all multiplication and division facts up to 10 x 10

■ use the multiplication facts to derive multiplication facts involving decimals

Success criteria

Can the children…

☐ respond quickly to the multiplication question shown on screen?

☐ find related division facts?

How to use the material for discussion

By the time they have reached Year 6 pupils will have constructed the multiplication tables up to 10 x 10 and will have found the corresponding division facts. They will have practised rapid recall of the facts and can now use their knowledge of tables and place value to calculate multiplication facts involving decimals.

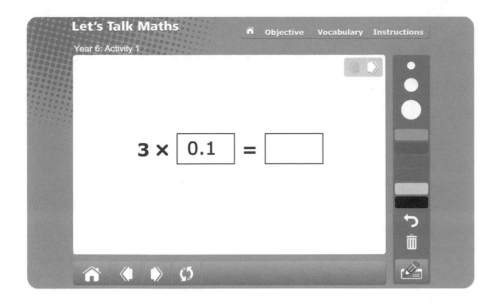

This activity could open with questions of the following type:

- Can you multiply decimals?
- How quickly can you answer this question?

Ask the pupils to take turns to come to the whiteboard to work out multiplication questions. You may wish to set a time challenge for them to answer each question. Can they beat the calculator? (Where one pupil uses the calculator and another works mentally.) Alternatively you could ask them to see how many questions that they can answer in one minute.

On another occasion ask the pupils to find the answer to one question then to create a division fact related to that question. For example the question 0.3 x 6 has the answer 1.8, which the pupils can then use to create two possible division questions: 1.8 ÷ 6 and 1.8 ÷ 0.3.

This activity also provides a useful opportunity to extend pupils' vocabulary:

- 1.8 is the product of 0.3 and 6
- 1.8 is a multiple of 0.3
- 6 is the quotient when 1.8 is divided by 0.3 (0.3 is the divisor)
- 0.3 is the quotient when 1.8 is divided by 6 (6 is the divisor)

Appropriate vocabulary

pair	multiply	divide
equals	times	product
quotient	calculate	calculation
operation	answer	multiple
divisor	square number	inverse

Use knowledge of place value and multiplication facts to 10 x 10 to derive related division facts involving decimals

Building on previous learning

Before starting this unit check that the children can already:

☐ recall quickly multiplication facts up to 10 x 10

☐ use the multiplication facts to derive quickly corresponding division facts

☐ use the multiplication facts to derive multiplication facts involving decimals

Learning objectives

■ use the multiplication facts to derive division facts involving decimals

Learning outcomes

The children will be able to:

■ recall quickly all multiplication and division facts up to 10 x 10

■ use the multiplication facts to derive division facts involving decimals

Success criteria

Can the children…

☐ respond quickly to the division question shown on screen?

☐ find related multiplication facts?

☐ recognise that division is the inverse operation to multiplication?

How to use the material for discussion

This activity is ideal to challenge higher ability pupils who have practised rapid recall of multiplication and division facts with integers and can now use their knowledge of tables and place value to calculate division facts involving decimals. Some of the questions are extremely difficult: for example 6.3 ÷ 0.9. With this type of question you may like pupils to investigate how to find the answer before you suggest multiplying both numbers by 10: 63 ÷ 9 is an easier question to understand and will give the same answer.

Let's Talk Maths

Objective   Vocabulary   Instructions

Year 6: Activity 2

$$6.3 \div 0.9 =$$

$$6.3 \div 0.3 =$$

$$8.1 \div 9 \ =$$

This activity could open with questions of the following type:

- Can you divide decimals?
- How quickly can you answer all three questions?

Ask the pupils to take turns to come to the screen to generate division questions. You may wish to set a time challenge for them to answer each set of questions. Can they beat the calculator? (Where one pupil uses the calculator and another works mentally.) Alternatively you could ask them to see how many questions that they can answer in one minute.

Appropriate vocabulary

pair	multiply	divide
equals	times	product
quotient	calculate	calculation
operation	answer	multiple
divisor	inverse	

Calculate mentally with decimals:
U.t + U.t, U.t - U.t

Building on previous learning

Before starting this unit check that the children can already:

- [ ] add or subtract mentally pairs of two-digit whole numbers
- [ ] use decimal notation for tenths and hundredths and partition decimals
- [ ] position one-place and two-place decimals on a number line
- [ ] use knowledge of place value and addition and subtraction of two-digit numbers to derive sums and differences of decimals

Learning objectives

- Calculate mentally with decimals:
  U.t + U.t, U.t - U.t

Learning outcomes

The children will be able to:

- add pairs of decimal numbers
- find the difference between pairs of decimal numbers
- use appropriate vocabulary
- talk confidently about the numbers

Success criteria

Can the children…

- [ ] add pairs of decimal numbers?
- [ ] subtract pairs of decimal numbers?
- [ ] listen and talk confidently using some of the vocabulary listed and some of the question types shown?

How to use the material for discussion

Children will add together and find the difference between decimal numbers. As with all of the activities the teacher can start the discussion using appropriate vocabulary and questions but should then encourage the pupils to take turns in leading the discussion. This activity can be repeated regularly and would be very useful as a lesson starter.

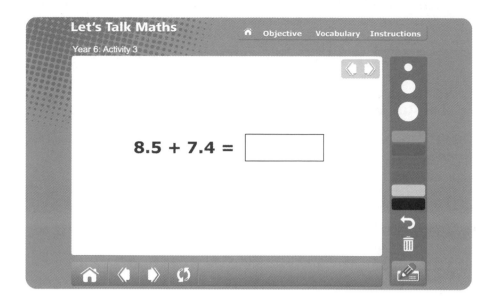

The activity consists of the teacher, or a pupil playing the role of leader, asking pupils to answer questions. Pupils give the answer orally and need to check each other's answers – this is a valuable part of the discussion.

Encourage the children to explain how they could add the first pair of numbers together. Are they going to add the ones first? Are they going to add the tenths first? Are they going to add the ones from the second number to the first number, then add the tenths? Are they going to add the tenths from the second number to the first number, then add the ones? Which way do they find quickest?

Now encourage the children to explain how they could find the difference between the second pair of numbers. Are they going to count on in tenths and ones from the smaller to the greater number? Are they going to count back? Are they going to use an empty number line? Which way do they find quickest?

Appropriate vocabulary

calculate	calculation	equation
operation	answer	method
explain	reasoning	pattern
predict	reason	rule
place value	partition	digit
two-digit number	three-digit number	add
sum	total	plus
sequence	decimal point	decimal place
ones	tenths	difference
minus	subtract	

Calculate mentally with integers: TU x U

Building on previous learning

Before starting this unit check that the children can already:

☐ recall quickly multiplication facts up to 10 x 10

☐ use the multiplication facts to derive quickly corresponding division facts

Learning objectives

- use the multiplication facts to calculate mentally with integers: TU x U

Learning outcomes

The children will be able to:

- recall quickly all multiplication and division facts up to 10 x 10

- use the multiplication facts to calculate mentally with integers: TU x U

- use appropriate vocabulary related to multiplication

Success criteria

Can the children…

☐ respond quickly to the multiplication question shown on screen?

☐ find related division facts?

☐ use the appropriate vocabulary?

How to use the material for discussion

By the time they have reached Year 6, pupils will have constructed the multiplication tables up to 10 x 10 and will have found the corresponding division facts. They will have practised rapid recall of the facts and can now use their knowledge of tables and place value to calculate mentally with integers: TU x U.

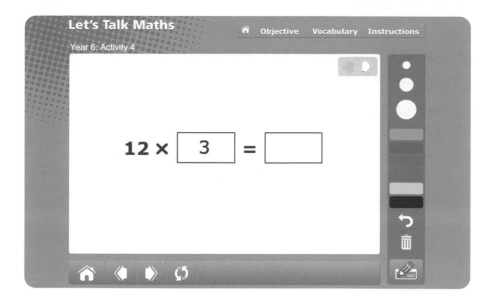

This activity could open with questions of the following type:

- Can you multiply two-digit integers by one-digit integers?
- How quickly can you answer this question?

Ask the pupils to take turns to come to the whiteboard to work out multiplication questions. You may wish to set a time challenge for them to answer each question. Can they beat the calculator? (Where one pupil uses the calculator and another works mentally.) Alternatively you could ask them to see how many questions that they can answer in one minute.

Ask the pupils to find the answer to one question then to create a division fact related to that question. For example the question 12 x 3 has the answer 36, which the pupils can then use to create two possible division questions: 36 ÷ 3 and 36 ÷ 12.

This activity also provides a useful opportunity to revise vocabulary:

- 102 is the product of 17 and 6
- 102 is a multiple of 17
- 102 is a multiple of 6
- 6 and 17 are both factors of 102
- 6 is the quotient when 102 is divided by 17 (17 is the divisor)
- 17 is the quotient when 102 is divided by 6 (6 is the divisor)
- 6, 17 and 102 are all integers (whole numbers)

Appropriate vocabulary

pair	multiply	integer
equals	times	product
answer	calculate	calculation
operation	multiple	factor

Calculate mentally with integers: TU ÷ U

Building on previous learning

Before starting this unit check that the children can already:

☐ recall quickly multiplication facts up to 10 x 10

☐ use the multiplication facts to derive quickly corresponding division facts

☐ calculate mentally with integers: TU x U

Learning objectives

- use the multiplication and division facts to calculate mentally with integers: TU ÷ U
- recognise that prime numbers have only two factors

Learning outcomes

The children will be able to:

- recall quickly all multiplication and division facts up to 10 x 10
- use the multiplication and division facts to calculate mentally with integers: TU ÷ U
- recognise prime numbers
- use appropriate vocabulary related to division

Success criteria

Can the children…

☐ respond quickly to the division question shown on screen?

☐ find remainders where appropriate?

☐ identify prime numbers?

☐ use the appropriate vocabulary?

How to use the material for discussion

By the time they have reached Year 6 pupils will have constructed the multiplication tables up to 10 x 10 and will have found the corresponding division facts. They will have practised rapid recall of the facts and can now use their knowledge of tables and place value to calculate mentally with integers: TU ÷ U.

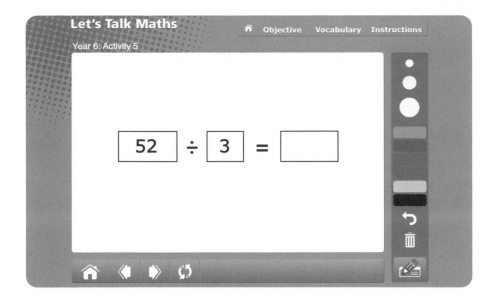

Ask the pupils to take turns to come to the whiteboard to work out division questions. Note that many of the questions will result in a remainder. Remind pupils that the number being divided is known as the dividend; the number by which it is being divided is the divisor; and the numerical result of the division question is the quotient.

You may wish to set a time challenge for them to answer each question. Can they beat the calculator? (Where one pupil uses the calculator and another works mentally.) Alternatively you could ask them to see how many questions that they can answer in one minute.

Ask the pupils to spot the prime numbers. These numbers will always have a remainder when they are divided by another integer.

Appropriate vocabulary

pair	multiply	integer
equals	times	product
answer	calculate	calculation
operation	multiple	factor
quotient	remainder	divisor
divisible by	dividend	prime number

Recognise that prime numbers have only two factors and identify prime numbers less than 100

Building on previous learning

Before starting this unit check that the children can already:

- [ ] recall quickly multiplication facts up to 10 x 10
- [ ] use the multiplication facts to derive quickly corresponding division facts
- [ ] identify pairs of factors of two-digit integers and find common multiples

Learning objectives

- recognise that prime numbers have only two factors
- identify prime numbers less than 100

Learning outcomes

The children will be able to:

- recall quickly all multiplication and division facts up to 10 x 10
- find multiples of integers beyond the tenth multiple
- define prime numbers
- find common multiples
- identify all prime numbers less than 100

Success criteria

Can the children…

- [ ] define prime numbers?
- [ ] find multiples of 2, 3, 5 and 7, including those that extend beyond the tenth multiple?
- [ ] find common multiples of two or more numbers?
- [ ] identify all prime numbers less than 100

How to use the material for discussion

This activity encourages pupils to extend their knowledge of multiples beyond those found in the multiplication tables. Pupils are introduced to appropriate vocabulary in relation to multiples, factors and prime numbers.

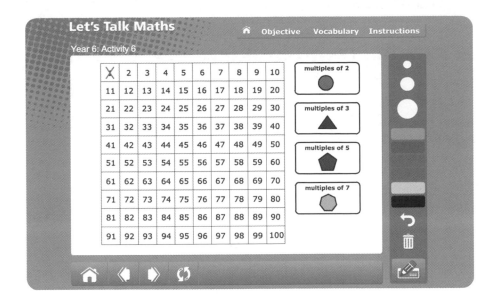

As a first step ensure that the children in the group understand that prime numbers are numbers with only two factors: the number itself and 1.

Explain to the children that they will be finding all of the prime numbers less than 100 by using the 'sieve of Eratostenes'. Eratostenes was a Greek astronomer who lived over 2000 years ago. What do they notice about the grid? Why is the number 1 crossed out? (because it is not a prime number).

Ask the children to take turns to label the multiples. One pupil can drag the red circles to all the multiples of 2 (except for 2 itself as it is a prime number). Other pupils can drag the triangles to the multiples of 3 (except for 3 itself as it is prime), the pentagons to the multiples of 5 (except for 5 itself as it is prime) and the heptagons to the multiples of 7 (except for 7 itself as it is prime). In each case the multiples will extend beyond the usual multiplication tables facts and deciding which numbers are multiples of 2, 3, 5 and 7 will provide opportunities for discussion.

Once all the multiples have been identified, encourage the children to discuss numbers that are multiples of, for example, 2 and 3 – these are known as common multiples of 2 and 3. Can the pupils find the common multiples of 3 and 5? 3 and 7? 5 and 7? etc.

Are there any numbers on the square that are common multiples of 2, 3 and 7? 3, 5 and 7?

Now ask the children to look at the numbers that do not have any coloured shapes on them. These are the prime numbers less than 100.

Appropriate vocabulary

integer	multiple	factor
prime number	common factor	circle
triangle	pentagon	heptagon

Calculate mentally with integers and decimals: U.t x U

Building on previous learning

Before starting this unit check that the children can already:

☐ recall quickly multiplication facts up to 10 x 10

☐ use the multiplication facts to derive quickly corresponding division facts

Learning objectives

■ Use the multiplication facts to calculate mentally with integers and decimals: U.t x U

Learning outcomes

The children will be able to:

■ recall quickly all multiplication and division facts up to 10 x 10

■ use the multiplication facts to calculate mentally with integers and decimals: U.t x U

■ use appropriate vocabulary related to multiplication

Success criteria

Can the children…

☐ respond quickly to the multiplication question shown on screen?

☐ find related division facts?

☐ use the appropriate vocabulary?

How to use the material for discussion

By the time they have reached Year 6 pupils will have constructed the multiplication tables up to 10 x 10 and will have found the corresponding division facts. They will have practised rapid recall of the facts and can now use their knowledge of tables and place value to calculate mentally with integers and decimals: U.t x U.

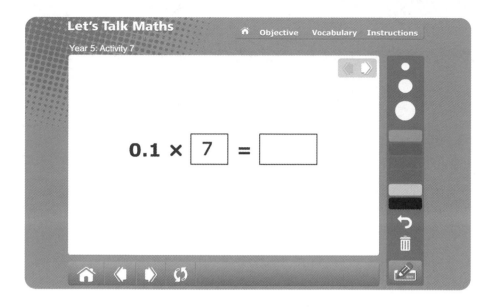

Ask the pupils to take turns to come to the whiteboard to work out multiplication questions. You may wish to set a time challenge for them to answer each question. Can they beat the calculator? (Where one pupil uses the calculator and another works mentally.) Alternatively you could ask them to see how many questions that they can answer in one minute.

You could discuss techniques with the children:

One method that they could use is to remove the decimal point, multiply then put the decimal point back in. For example, to calculate 2.9 x 6 it may be easier to calculate 29 x 6 to reach 174 then to replace the decimal point to find the answer 17.4 Pupils need to understand why this works - can they explain it? Can they see that effectively the 2.9 has been multiplied by 10 to make 29 and that therefore they need to divide the final answer by 10 as division is the inverse of multiplication?

Some children may prefer to multiply the separate elements of the 2.9 by 6 then combine the results: 2 x 6 = 12 and 0.9 x 6 = 5.4   12 + 5.4 = 17.4

Appropriate vocabulary

pair	multiply	integer
equals	times	product
answer	calculate	calculation
operation	multiple	factor
decimal place	decimal point	inverse

Calculate mentally with integers and decimals: U.t ÷ U

Building on previous learning

Before starting this unit check that the children can already:

☐ recall quickly multiplication facts up to 10 x 10

☐ use the multiplication facts to derive quickly corresponding division facts

☐ calculate mentally with integers: TU ÷ U

Learning objectives

■ use the multiplication and division facts to calculate mentally with integers and decimals: U.t ÷ U

Learning outcomes

The children will be able to:

■ recall quickly all multiplication and division facts up to 10 x 10

■ use the multiplication and division facts to calculate mentally with integers and decimals: U.t ÷ U

■ use appropriate vocabulary related to division

Success criteria

Can the children…

☐ respond quickly to the division question shown on screen?

☐ use the appropriate vocabulary?

How to use the material for discussion

This activity extends the work covered in Year 6 Activity 2. Pupils can now use their knowledge of tables and place value to calculate mentally with integers: TU ÷ U.

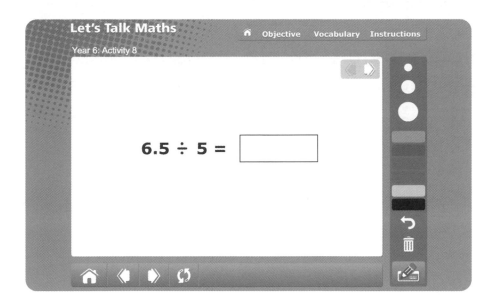

This activity could open with questions of the following type:

- Can you divide decimal numbers with one decimal place by one-digit integers?
- How quickly can you answer all four questions?

Ask the pupils to take turns to come to the whiteboard to work out division questions. You may wish to set a time challenge for them to answer each set of questions. Can they beat the calculator? (Where one pupil uses the calculator and another works mentally.) Alternatively you could ask them to see how many questions that they can answer in one minute.

Appropriate vocabulary

pair	multiply	integer
equals	times	product
answer	calculate	calculation
operation	multiple	factor
quotient	remainder	divisor
divisible by	dividend	prime number

Find the difference between a positive and a negative integer, or two negative integers, in context

Building on previous learning

Before starting this unit check that the children can already:

☐ count from any given number in whole number and decimal steps, extending beyond zero when counting backwards.

☐ relate any given number to its position on a number line

Learning objectives

■ Find the difference between a positive and a negative integer, or two negative integers, in context

■ Read and interpret scales on a range of measuring instruments

Learning outcomes

The children will be able to:

■ read and interpret scales on thermometers

■ find the difference between two positive integers in relation to temperature

■ find the difference between a positive and a negative integer in relation to temperature

■ find the difference between two negative integers in relation to temperature

Success criteria

Can the children…

☐ read the temperatures shown on the thermometers on the screen?

☐ find the differences between temperatures shown by the thermometers on the screen?

☐ use the appropriate vocabulary?

How to use the material for discussion

The pupils' task is to find the difference between the two temperatures. Sometimes, of course, both temperatures are above zero, sometimes one of them is below zero and sometimes both are below zero. This provides lots of opportunities for discussion.

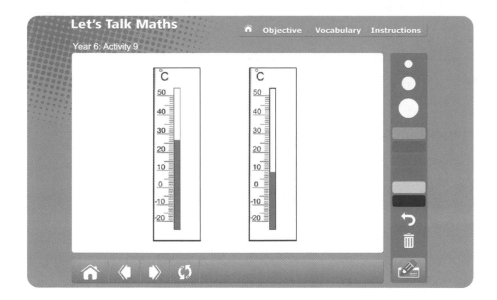

Ask the pupils to take turns to come to the whiteboard to change different temperatures on the thermometers. Encourage them to look at each thermometer and comment on the temperature shown: Could that temperature be recorded in this country? Is it too hot for this country? Is it too cold for this country? At what time of year could it be? Ensure that the children can read the temperatures accurately and that they state them in full, ie using 'degrees Celsius'.

Once you are confident that the children can read the temperatures accurately ask them to find the difference in temperatures between those shown on the two thermometers.

Appropriate vocabulary

calculate	calculation	operation
answer	method	strategy
explain	positive	negative
compare	greater than	less than
subtract	difference	minus
degree	Celsius	

Blocks C and revision

Describe and interpret results and solutions to problems using the mode, range, median and mean

Building on previous learning

Before starting this unit check that the children can already:

☐ find and interpret the mode of a set of data

☐ read and interpret scales on thermometers

☐ find the difference between two positive integers in relation to temperature

Learning objectives

- Describe and interpret results and solutions to problems using the mode, range, median and mean

Learning outcomes

The children will be able to:

- find the mode of a set of temperatures
- find the range of a set of temperatures
- find the median of a set of temperatures
- find the mean of a set of temperatures
- make comparisons between the mode, range, median and mean of different sets of temperatures

Success criteria

Can the children…

☐ interpret the data shown on the temperature charts?

☐ use the appropriate vocabulary?

How to use the material for discussion

A temperature chart showing temperatures in three different cities one week in February will be displayed. The pupils' task is to make comparisons between the mode, range, median and mean of the different sets of temperatures. This provides lots of opportunities for discussion.

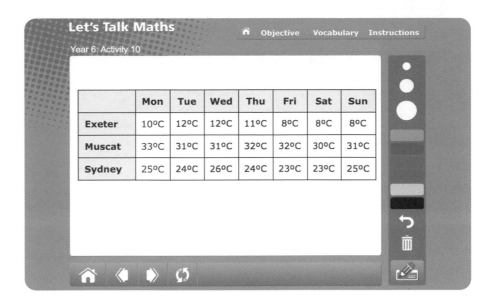

Encourage the children to ask lots of questions of each other:

- What is the highest temperature shown on the chart?
- What is the lowest temperature shown on the chart?
- What is the range of temperatures on the chart?
- What is the range of temperatures in Exeter? Muscat? Sydney?
- What is the mode of the temperatures in Exeter? Muscat? Sydney? Note: pupils should notice that there is not a mode for the Sydney temperatures.
- What is the median of the temperatures in Exeter? Muscat? Sydney? (You may need to remind pupils to put the temperatures in order, then to find the middle value.)
- What is the mean of the temperatures in Exeter? Muscat? Sydney?

Can the pupils find all three cities on a world map or globe?

Appropriate vocabulary

calculate	calculation	operation
answer	method	strategy
explain	positive	negative
compare	greater than	less than
subtract	difference	minus
degree	Celsius	mode
range	median	mean
average		

Calculate the perimeter and area of rectilinear shapes

Building on previous learning

Before starting this unit check that the children can already:

- [ ] calculate mentally with integers and decimals
- [ ] use efficient written methods to add integers and decimals
- [ ] use a calculator to solve problems involving multi-step calculations
- [ ] calculate the perimeter of regular and irregular polygons
- [ ] use the formula for the area of a rectangle

Learning objectives

- Calculate the perimeter and area of rectilinear shapes
- Solve multi-step problems, and problems involving decimals
- Choose and use appropriate calculation strategies at each stage, including calculator use
- Convert between units using decimals to two places (eg change 95cm to 0.95m)

Learning outcomes

The children will be able to:

- calculate the perimeter of rectilinear shapes
- calculate the area of rectilinear shapes
- solve multi-step problems involving perimeter and area
- convert measurements in centimetres to metres
- discuss area and perimeter confidently

Success criteria

Can the children...

- [ ] find perimeters of squares, rectangles and shapes created from squares?
- [ ] convert centimetres to metres?
- [ ] convert square centimetres to square metres?
- [ ] work systematically to solve multi-step problems?

How to use the material for discussion

A pile of paving slabs are displayed which the pupils can drag together to create a 'patio'. Their task is to find the perimeter and area of the patio. You may decide to ask the pupils to start with just two slabs so that they can begin to see the processes involved.

Note that this activity could form an extended investigation.

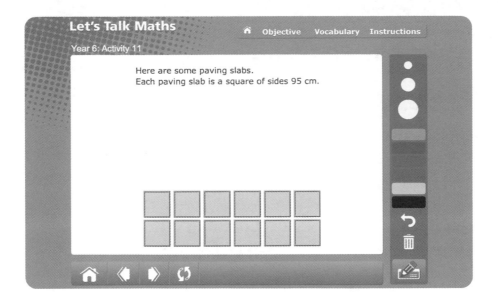

Pupils should discuss their strategies to find the perimeter and area of the patio. The perimeter can be found, of course, by adding the number of slab edges that can be found round the edge of the patio and multiplying by the length of the slab, but the pupils will have to decide whether to present the perimeter in centimetres or in metres. This will involve converting between units.

A more difficult challenge is to find the area. If working with just two or three paving slabs, you could ask the children to find the area in square centimetres then to convert this to square metres – what number should they divide by? Some will immediately suggest dividing by 100 – can they see why they actually need to divide by 100^2? If working with more than two or three slabs you could encourage the pupils to find the area in square metres straight away.

This activity can be extended by asking the pupils to create a patio of a different shape with the 12 slabs. Which shape will have the smallest perimeter? What do you notice about the area?

Further developments of the activity include not using all of the slabs or using all of the slabs but leaving one or more gaps in the middle.

Appropriate vocabulary

calculate	calculation	operation
answer	method	strategy
explain	area	perimeter
length	distance	square centimetre
square metre		

Calculate angles in a triangle

Building on previous learning

Before starting this unit check that the children can already:

☐ estimate and measure acute and obtuse angles using a protractor to a suitable degree of accuracy

Learning objectives

- Calculate angles in a triangle

Learning outcomes

The children will be able to:

- identify whether an angle is acute or obtuse
- make reasonable estimates of sizes of angles
- calculate the size of a missing angle where two angles in a triangle are provided

Success criteria

Can the children…

☐ identify whether an angle is acute or obtuse?

☐ make reasonable estimates of sizes of angles?

☐ use appropriate vocabulary in relation to measurement of angles?

☐ calculate the size of a missing angle where two angles in a triangle are provided?

☐ identify the special features of equilateral triangles and isosceles triangles?

How to use the material for discussion

If necessary give the pupils some practice in measuring angles using a protractor by revising Year 5 Activity 16. Having experienced measuring angles with a protractor the pupils should now be skilled in estimating the sizes of angles. They will be aware that angles in a triangle have a total measurement of 180°. This activity provides practice in subtracting from 180 to find the size of an angle where two angles in a triangle are provided.

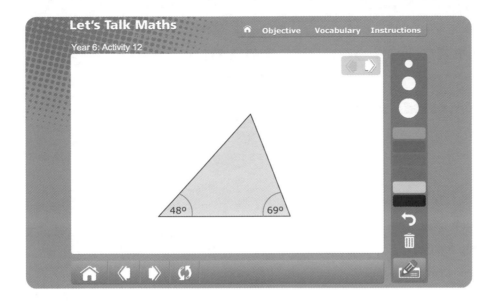

Ask the children to state whether the angles shown are acute (between 0° and 90°) or obtuse (between 90° and 180°) then to state whether the missing angle is acute or obtuse. Now ask the children to find the size of the missing angle – they may not realise at first that it can be found by adding the two angles provided then subtracting the sum of these angles from 180°. If necessary you could provide the children with calculators but, if possible, encourage them to calculate using mental methods.

Now ask one of the children to become the leader of the discussion.

Note that two of the triangles generated by the computer are equilateral – pupils should notice that all of their angles are equal. Some of the triangles generated are isosceles – pupils should notice that, not only are two sides of the same length, but also that two angles are equal in size.

Appropriate vocabulary

measure	angle	protractor
approximate	estimate	degree
right angle	acute	obtuse
subtract	triangle	isosceles
equilateral		

Calculate angles around a point

Building on previous learning

Before starting this unit check that the children can already:

☐ estimate and measure acute and obtuse angles using a protractor to a suitable degree of accuracy

☐ calculate angles in a straight line

Learning objectives

■ Calculate angles around a point

Learning outcomes

The children will be able to:

■ identify whether an angle is acute, obtuse or reflex

■ make reasonable estimates of sizes of angles

■ calculate the size of a missing angle where one angle around a point is provided

Success criteria

Can the children…

☐ identify whether an angle is acute, obtuse or reflex?

☐ make reasonable estimates of sizes of angles?

☐ use appropriate vocabulary in relation to measurement of angles?

☐ calculate the size of a missing angle where one angle around a point is provided?

How to use the material for discussion

If necessary give the pupils some practice in measuring angles using a protractor by revising Year 5 Activity 16. Having experienced measuring angles with a protractor the pupils should now be skilled in estimating the sizes of angles. They will be aware that angles around a point have a total measurement of 360°. This activity provides practice in subtracting from 360 to find the size of an angle where one angle around a point is provided.

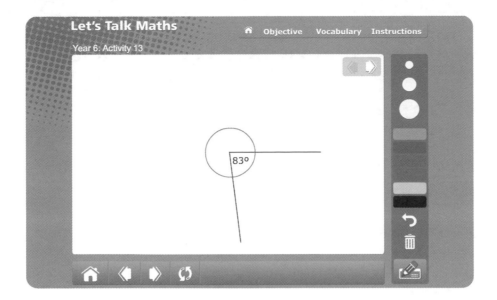

Ask the children to state whether the angle shown is acute (between 0° and 90°), obtuse (between 90° and 180°) or reflex (between 180° and 360°) then to state whether the missing angle is acute, obtuse or reflex. Now ask the children to find the size of the missing angle – they may not realise at first that it can be found by subtracting the size of the given angle from 360°. If necessary you could provide the children with calculators but, if possible, encourage them to calculate using mental methods.

Now ask one of the children to become the leader of the discussion.

Appropriate vocabulary

measure	angle	protractor
approximate	estimate	degree
right angle	acute	obtuse
subtract	reflex	

Describe, identify and visualise parallel and perpendicular edges; use these properties to classify 2-D shapes

Building on previous learning

Before starting this unit check that the children can already:

☐ identify, visualise and describe properties of rectangles, triangles, regular polygons

☐ use knowledge of properties to draw 2-D shapes

Learning objectives

■ Describe, identify and visualise parallel and perpendicular edges

■ Use these properties to classify 2-D shapes

Learning outcomes

The children will be able to:

■ identify 2-D shapes on screen

■ use appropriate vocabulary to refer to the properties of the shapes

■ identify, visualise, draw, make and describe the following shapes: square, scalene triangle, right-angled triangle, isosceles triangle, equilateral triangle, rectangle, parallelogram, rhombus, kite, trapezium

Success criteria

Can the children…

☐ identify 2-D shapes, using appropriate vocabulary to refer to their properties?

☐ visualise, draw, make and describe a square, scalene triangle, right-angled triangle, isosceles triangle, equilateral triangle, rectangle, parallelogram, rhombus, kite, trapezium?

How to use the material for discussion

A selection of the following 2-D shapes will be displayed: square, scalene triangle, right-angled triangle, isosceles triangle, equilateral triangle, rectangle, parallelogram, rhombus, kite, trapezium. The task is for the pupils to identify the shape and describe its properties, including whether it has any parallel or perpendicular edges. They should be able to make clear distinctions between each different type of triangle and between each different type of quadrilateral.

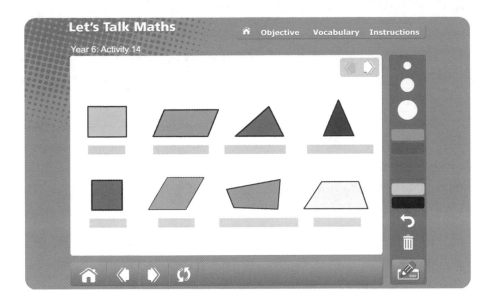

Ask one of the children to describe one property that the first shape possesses, eg the number of edges or the number of vertices (but not the name of the shape). Ask another pupil to describe a different property of the shape. Encourage the children to state whether any of the edges are equal in length, whether the shape has any parallel lines, whether any of the edges are perpendicular to each other. Once all the properties of the shape have been discussed ask the pupils to give the name of the shape and click on the grey box below the shape to reveal the name. Note that there are several quadrilaterals, including squares and rectangles in different orientations.

Now ask one of the children to become the leader of the discussion for the next shape.

Appropriate vocabulary

polygon	perpendicular	parallel
regular	irregular	edge
vertex	vertices	kite
parallelogram	trapezium	rhombus
quadrilateral	triangle	isosceles
equilateral	scalene	rectangle
square		

Make and draw shapes with increasing accuracy and apply knowledge of their properties: circles

Building on previous learning

Before starting this unit check that the children can already:

- [ ] identify, visualise and describe properties of rectangles, triangles, regular polygons
- [ ] use knowledge of properties to draw 2-D shapes

Learning objectives

- Make and draw shapes with increasing accuracy and apply knowledge of their properties: circles

Learning outcomes

The children will be able to:

- use appropriate vocabulary to refer to the properties of the circles
- calculate the diameter when the radius is supplied
- calculate the radius when the diameter is supplied

Success criteria

Can the children…

- [ ] use appropriate vocabulary to refer to the properties of the circles shown on screen: radius, diameter, circumference, centre?
- [ ] calculate the diameter when the radius is supplied?
- [ ] calculate the radius when the diameter is supplied?

How to use the material for discussion

The pupils' task is to use appropriate vocabulary to refer to the properties of the circle shown. They should follow this activity by drawing some circles and identifying the diameter and radius of each one. As an extension activity you may like to ask the children to find the approximate length of the circumference of each circle and to compare this to its diameter – do they notice that the circumference is approximately three times the diameter?

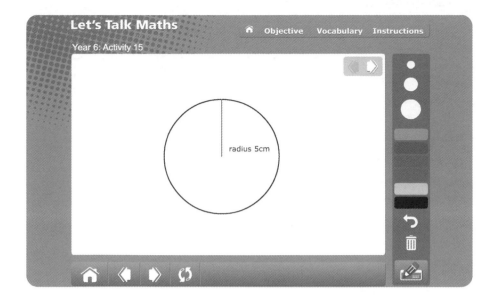

Point out that the screen shows a picture of a circle with a specified radius or diameter measured in centimetres, but that the picture itself is on a larger scale – the children could try drawing a copy of the circle using the radius or diameter accurately. Ask the children what they can see, encouraging them to state that it is a circle and that either a radius is shown or a diameter is shown. They should be able to state that the radius is a line drawn from the centre to the circumference (edge). They should be able to state that a diameter is double the length of a radius and that it passes through the centre and therefore they should be able to calculate the diameter when the radius is supplied and vice versa.

Now ask one of the children to become the leader of the discussion for the next circle.

Appropriate vocabulary

circle	radius	diameter
circumference	centre	

Express a larger whole number as a fraction of a smaller one

Building on previous learning

Before starting this unit check that the children can already:

☐ express a smaller whole number as a fraction of a larger one
(eg recognise that 5 out of 8 is $\frac{5}{8}$)

Learning objectives

■ Express a larger whole number as
a fraction of a smaller one

Learning outcomes

The children will be able to:

■ use appropriate vocabulary to refer to
mixed numbers and improper fractions

■ relate the correct mixed number to a
picture showing whole and part shapes

■ convert mixed numbers to their
equivalent improper fractions

■ convert improper fractions to their
equivalent mixed numbers

Success criteria

Can the children...

☐ use appropriate vocabulary to refer to mixed numbers and improper fractions?

☐ convert mixed numbers to their equivalent improper fractions?

☐ convert improper fractions to their equivalent mixed numbers?

How to use the material for discussion

Different numbers of pizzas will be displayed, where there are whole and part
pizzas. The pupils' task is to state what the appropriate mixed number is that is
represented by the picture and then to convert the mixed number to its equivalent
improper fraction.

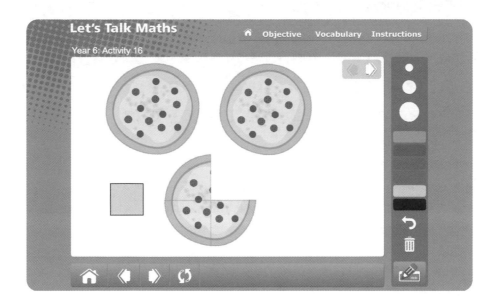

The first time that you complete this activity ask the pupils to identify simply how many pizzas they can see. For example there may be $1\frac{5}{8}$ pizzas. Explain that $1\frac{5}{8}$ is known as a mixed number because it is a mixture of an integer and a fraction. Now ask the question how many eighths there are altogether – the pupils should state that there are 13 because the whole one can be cut into 8 eighths and there are five eighths in the part pizza. Show the pupils how this can be written as $\frac{13}{8}$ and explain that this is known as an improper fraction because the numerator is larger than the denominator.

Now ask one of the children to become the leader of the discussion.

Appropriate vocabulary

fraction	proper fraction	improper fraction
mixed number	numerator	denominator
equivalent		

Solve multi-step problems involving decimals; choose and use appropriate calculation strategies at each stage, including calculator use

Building on previous learning

Before starting this unit check that the children can already:

☐ derive and recall all addition and subtraction facts for each number to at least 20

☐ derive and recall sums and differences of multiples of 10, 100 or 1000

☐ derive and recall all number pairs that total 100

☐ recall quickly multiplication facts up to 10 x 10

☐ use the multiplication facts to derive quickly corresponding division facts

☐ use knowledge of rounding, place value, number facts and inverse operations to estimate and check calculations

Learning objectives

■ Solve multi-step problems involving decimals

■ Choose and use appropriate calculation strategies at each stage, including calculator use

Learning outcomes

The children will be able to:

■ solve problems involving adding in the context of money

■ solve problems involving subtracting in the context of money

■ solve problems involving multiplying in the context of money

■ solve problems involving dividing in the context of money

■ solve multi-step problems involving money

Success criteria

Can the children...

☐ use addition and/or multiplication to find total amounts?

☐ use subtraction to make comparisons between two amounts?

☐ use division to share amounts equally?

☐ choose and use appropriate calculation strategies, including calculator use?

☐ use the calculator efficiently and interpret the display correctly in the context of money?

☐ use appropriate vocabulary in relation to spending money and finding change?

How to use the material for discussion

The chart provides many opportunities for the discussion of extended activities involving solving problems using all four rules. The task for the pupils is to create some problems that they can ask other children to solve – they will need to be very precise in their language. The focus of the work must be oral, so the children will need to speak clearly using appropriate vocabulary. This activity is well suited for the use of a calculator.

This activity provides many opportunities for creating and solving problems. You could ask the children to create some problems for others to solve. Here are some ideas:

- What is the total cost for an adult to buy a ticket, a large popcorn and a fizzy drink?
- Ed, who is 24 years old, bought a ticket to see a film and a box of popcorn. The total cost was £9.74. What size popcorn did he buy?
- Nancy bought fizzy drinks for 5 people. All the fizzy drinks were the same size and the total cost was £13.75. What size drink did she buy?

Appropriate vocabulary

more	less	total
cost	altogether	difference
price	change	double
answer	explain	operation
pound	penny	pence
coin	add	subtract
multiply	double	calculate
note	calculator	more expensive
less expensive	compare	

Construct and interpret bar charts with grouped discrete data

Building on previous learning

Before starting this unit check that the children can already:

☐ construct frequency tables, pictograms and bar and line graphs

Learning objectives

■ Construct and interpret bar charts with grouped discrete data

Learning outcomes

The children will be able to:

■ interpret the title, labelling and calibration of a bar chart, including where each interval represents a range of data (grouped discrete data)

■ interpret the data on a bar chart with grouped discrete data

Success criteria

Can the children…

☐ use appropriate vocabulary in relation to the structure of a bar chart?

☐ interpret the data on a bar chart where the data is grouped?

☐ conduct a survey and draw appropriate charts showing the results?

How to use the material for discussion

The chart provides many opportunities for discussion. It is essential that pupils understand the calibration of the chart. They should be able to point out each element of the structure of the chart: the title, the labels, etc., as well as to be able to interpret the data then to conduct their own survey to find data on the same subject.

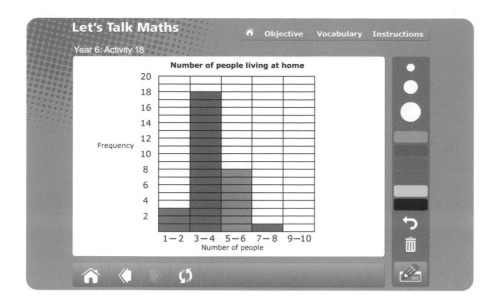

Ask the children to describe the bar chart, but not referring to the data it shows. They should refer to the horizontal axis or x-axis; the vertical axis or y-axis; the title; the labels of each axis; the intervals along the x-axis and the divisions along the y-axis.

Now ask them to discuss the data. What is each bar showing? Eg, the first bar shows a home with 1–2 people living there: this could be three adults or one adult and two children, etc. Are the results as expected? Note that you may have to explain the term 'frequency' to the children: the number of times that something occurs in a given sample.

After they have completed this activity orally the pupils could conduct their own survey in the class to create a bar chart of similar data.

Appropriate vocabulary

problem	solution	calculate
method	explain	classify
represent	analyse	interpret
data	information	survey
questionnaire	graph	chart
table	interval	division
horizontal axis	vertical axis	axes
label	title	bar chart
frequency	x-axis	y-axis

Published 2009 by A & C Black Publishers Limited
36 Soho Square, London W1D 3QY
www.acblack.com

ISBN 9781408111154

Copyright © A & C Black Publishers Limited
Written by Andrew Brodie
Page layout by Bob Vickers

A CIP record for this publication is available from the British Library.

Printed in Great Britain by Martins the Printers, Berwick-upon-Tweed.

This book is produced using paper that is made from wood grown in
managed, sustainable forests. It is natural, renewable and recyclable.
The logging and manufacturing processes conform to the environmental
regulations of the country of origin.

To see our full range of titles visit www.acblack.com